THE JURASSIC COAST - A MIGHTY TALE

First published in Great Britain 2014
by the Jurassic Coast Trust
Lulworth Estate Office, East Lulworth, Dorset BH20 5QS
www.jurassiccoast.org

ISBN 978-0-9931107-0-2

Written and illustrated by Tim Britton
Designed by Penny Saunders

Printed by Maslands Ltd, Tiverton, Devon. Printed on FSC paper using environmentally friendly vegetable-based inks.
Inside Cover Photo: Jurassic Coast Team

This MIGHTY TALE
is dedicated to everyone
who loves The Jurassic Coast
..past, present or future....

The Jurassic

... 250 million years

Coast

...a Mighty Tale

and 95 miles long....

...all told in just 58 pages by this PENCIL this BRUSH and this HAND...

3

It's a long thin narrow
steep and rocky tale to tell

...told from the tops of its cliffs...

...down to the shoreline at Low Tide.

Its the story of the making of Rock

from soft beginnings

piling up layer upon layer...

...and hardening into stone

6

of vast red baking deserts

of oceans rising...

...and falling

8

eroding
landscapes...

of ancient plants and
primeval trees

10

and early life cavorting

11

A tale of huge rivers

and the beds they left behind

now strewn across the
pages of this book.

...of forests growing up...

and dying down...

...adding yet more layers to the toothsome cake of TIME

A Record of Life evolving...

..of endless creativity and invention

of dimorphodons

...Iguanodons...

plesiosaurs

...icthyosaurs

19

...and of the Pliosaur mega predator of the Tethys Sea

and millions of.....

.....years later.....

.....of the creature.....

.....that evolved

..to give
everything
a
Name.

Yes. But measured
in Grannies...
...at
2 Grannies
every
100 Years...

...thats only about 5 million grannies .....

...nowhere near even The population of LONDON..

About 90 million grannies ago our SUN formed.

28

29

...and after many...

...changes of clothes...

30

...to form the world we know today...

"...and bring us...

...to the Coast.....

...that is our tale.

Its like the pages of a 95 mile long Book....

...in a crumbling library

...best viewed from the sea...

35

some pages stacked
in neat piles

others leaning

whole chapters borrowed
and never returned

...or slipped
into the sea.

their letters strewn across the beach... ₂

newer chapters hurled on top of much earlier ones...

"THE UNCONFORMITY"

..the missing ones in between called "The Unconformity"

Great chunks of the Book crumpled and twisted...

by some rude and illiterate vandal

39

Its a book thats
excited huge curiosity across
the Ages

from the
lowly lumpsucker

41

to the smartypant scientist

42

stone plants which grew from seeds embedded in the rocks?

The bones of mythical dragons
or of giant humans?

45

A story of famous fossil hunters...

and colossal eggheads

and of the Birthplace
of a new Science

If we could drop through all the layers of Time

such wonders would we see

Oops!... I'm running out of pages!

49

'So....
where will it all be
in another
5 million
grannies?.....

High up on some new mountain range? goggled at by some new species?

OR deep beneath some new Ocean...

full of
new life-forms?

Or will the fossilized remains of our Time here on Earth.

..be revealed on some
new coast...

...embedded in new rocks...

55

...evidence as ever of the unstoppable creativity of EVOLUTION....

here on the ever
shifting landforms ...

...of the Great Spinning Mother Earth.

Acknowledgements

The Jurassic Coast Trust is indebted to Tim Britton and Penny Saunders
for their creativity, bonhomie and time.

We are all immensely grateful to Sibyl King and the Fine Family Foundation,
Dorset and Devon County Councils for supporting Tim's film from which this
book came, and to the Fine Family Foundation again for supporting the book.

Finally we are grateful to Sam Rose for the original suggestion and Sam Scriven
for the knowledge.

You can watch the film of the book at www.jurassiccoast.org/mightytale

The Jurassic Coast

England's only natural World Heritage Site is a 95 mile long stretch of stunningly beautiful coastline, between Exmouth in East Devon and Studland Bay in Dorset. The rocks and fossils found in the cliffs present a near continuous record through geological history, from 250 million years ago to 65 million years ago, showing how the earth changed through the Triassic, Jurassic and Cretaceous periods of time; when dinosaurs ruled the earth.

This coastline was named as a World Heritage Site by the United Nations Educational, Scientific and Cultural Organisation (UNESCO) in 2001 because of its outstanding rocks, fossils and coastal landforms. The designation means it must be looked after for future generations. Find out more at www.jurassiccoast.org.

The Jurassic Coast Trust

Is a charity that inspires people to enjoy the Jurassic Coast and to safeguard it for future generations. We support education and conservation projects along the World Heritage Site and we try to involve individuals and communities in our work as much as possible.

We are delighted that the proceeds from this book will help us fund many more projects, like the Big Jurassic Classroom which helps school children understand the coast and learn from it. We love the Jurassic Coast and we're delighted to share our passion with you through the pages of Tim's wonderful book.